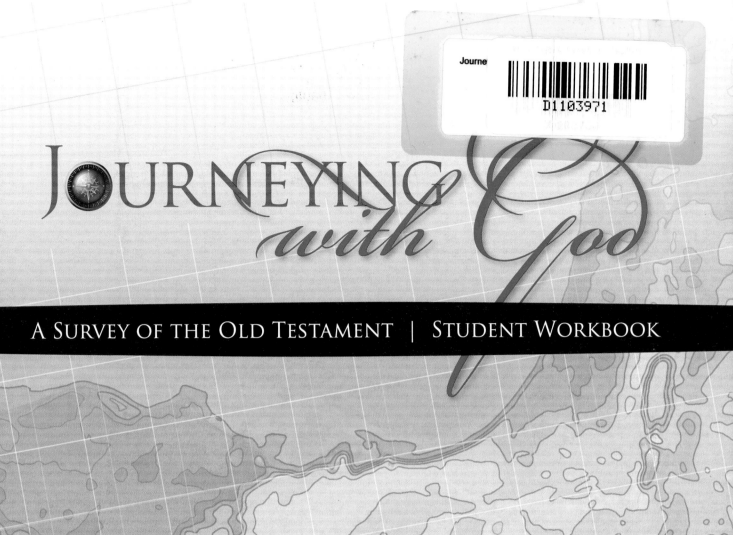

Journeying with God

A Survey of the Old Testament | Student Workbook

Purposeful Design Publications is the publishing division of the Association of Christian Schools International (ACSI) and is committed to the ministry of Christian school education, to enable Christian educators and schools worldwide to effectively prepare students for life. As the publisher of textbooks, trade books, and other educational resources within ACSI, Purposeful Design Publications strives to produce biblically sound materials that reflect Christian scholarship and stewardship and that address the identified needs of Christian schools around the world.

Unless otherwise identified, all Scripture quotations are taken from the Holy Bible, New International Version® (NIV®), © 1973, 1978, 1984 by International Bible Society. Used by permission of Zondervan Publishing House. All rights reserved.

The maps in this book are reproduced by permission from *Rose Book of Bible Charts, Maps and Timelines* (Torrance, CA: Rose Publishing, 2005).

Printed in the United States of America
15 14 13 12 11 10 09 08   1 2 3 4 5 6 7

Trull, Greg
    Journeying with God: A survey of the Old Testament
    ISBN 978-1-58331-216-2   Student workbook   Catalog #7075

Design: Michael Riester
Editorial team: John Conaway, Cheryl Chiapperino, Christina Nichols
Cover image courtesy Jacques Descloitres, MODIS Land Group, NASA GSFC

Purposeful Design Publications
A Division of ACSI
PO Box 65130 • Colorado Springs, CO 80962-5130
Customer Service: 800-367-0798   www.acsi.org

Contents

Please note that the Minor Prophets are not studied in the same order as they appear in the Bible. For the purposes of this course, these books have been grouped chronologically and geographically in order to help students link the books to one another and to the rest of the Old Testament.

Journeying with God

Course Introduction

Course Introduction

Welcome to *Journeying with God: A Survey of the Old Testament*. The Old Testament takes up most of the pages in the Bible. In this course, you will gain a new understanding of these thirty-nine Bible books.

Some Old Testament survey courses ask students to learn random facts about the Old Testament—and thirty-nine books can hold a lot of facts! But we can learn many facts and still not know what the Old Testament is all about. We need a big-picture view. We need to see that all the facts and people and events and stories in the Old Testament are part of one big story: *God's plan of salvation*. The story begins with the Creation and the Fall (Genesis), develops through God's activity in the rest of the Old Testament, reaches its peak with the life and death and resurrection of Jesus (the Gospels), and culminates in God's eternal plan for our future (Revelation). Studying the Old Testament helps us gain a fuller understanding of that great story.

Studying the Old Testament also has many personal benefits. It introduces us to people we can identify with—ordinary, imperfect people who trusted God and lived for Him in the nitty-gritty of everyday life. That same God, who never changes (Malachi 3:6), is worth trusting today.

In *Journeying with God*, you'll see how the people and events of the Old Testament fit into the big story of God's activity throughout history. Your understanding of the New Testament will become deeper and more insightful. And your relationship with Jesus will take on a richer meaning.

Bible Facts

There are sixty-six books in the Bible, written by forty authors over a period of 1,600 years. The Old Testament contains thirty-nine of those books. The Old Testament was written in Hebrew, with a few parts in Aramaic. The New Testament was written in Greek.

The Old Testament was written over a period of nearly 1,000 years. Moses wrote the first five books around 1440 BC; Malachi wrote around 440 BC.

The Old Testament books are organized like a library, with books of the same type grouped together. Each group has either five or twelve books. Here are the groupings of Old Testament books:

> Law (Pentateuch), five books
> History, twelve books
> Poetry, five books
> Major Prophets, five books
> Minor Prophets, twelve books

The Story of the Old Testament

During this course, you will learn many facts about the Old Testament. But the purpose of the course is not to memorize facts. The main emphasis of this course is the *story* of the Old Testament. The whole Bible tells one great story: *God's plan of salvation*. In the Old Testament, we see the beginning and middle of that story. In the New Testament, we read about the end of the story. And you'll understand the end of the story better after you've learned about what came before it.

Throughout history, Bible scholars have described the story of the Old Testament as a journey. (That's where the title of the course came from!) The people of God are journeying with Him toward their ultimate destination. But this is not an easy journey for God's people. When their relationship with God is going well, they are on a mountaintop. When they rebel and their relationship with God becomes cold and distant, they are in a valley. This sequence happens time and time again. In fact, the whole history of the Old Testament is a series of peaks and valleys, ups and downs— like a long roller-coaster ride!

On the following page is a brief overview of the Old Testament story, with its peaks and valleys.

PEAKS

Creation
Genesis 1–2

God created everything, including human beings, and His handiwork was declared "very good" (1:31).

Promise
Genesis 12–50

God told Abram to leave his homeland. God promised that the family of Abram would become a great nation and that "all peoples on earth" would be blessed through him (12:3).

Nation
Exodus 3–40, Leviticus

God delivered His people from Egypt and made a covenant with them at Sinai.

Conquest
Joshua

The obedience of Joshua and the new generation of Israelites led to the conquest of the Promised Land.

Failure
Genesis 3–11

Adam and Eve sinned. Soon, sin had pervaded all of God's creation.

Slavery
Exodus 1–2

God's people were slaves in Egypt. They cried out to God for help.

Wandering
Numbers, Deuteronomy

After two years in the wilderness, the Israelites came to the border of the Promised Land, but they turned back in unbelief. They wandered in the wilderness for another thirty-eight years.

VALLEYS

Kingdom
1 and 2 Samuel,
1 Kings 1–11,
1 Chronicles,
2 Chronicles 1–9,
Poetic books

David unified the kingdom
and wrote many psalms.
Solomon built the great
temple and wrote poetry
and wisdom books.

Judah
2 Kings 18–24,
2 Chronicles 29–35,
Jeremiah,
Habakkuk,
Zephaniah,
Nahum

After the defeat of the
northern kingdom, the
southern kingdom of Judah
was all that remained of the
once-great nation. This era
begins with the defeat and
captivity of Israel in 722 BC
and ends with the fall of
Jerusalem in 586 BC.

Return
Ezra,
Nehemiah,
Haggai,
Zechariah

These books record
how God brought
His exiled people
back to the Promised
Land.

Chaos
Judges,
Ruth

Israel's incomplete
obedience led to a series
of cycles that spiraled
down into spiritual chaos.

Division
1 Kings 12–22,
2 Kings 1–17,
2 Chronicles 10–28,
Isaiah,
Hosea,
Joel,
Amos,
Obadiah,
Jonah,
Micah

After Solomon died, the
nation split in two. The
northern kingdom was
called Israel; the southern
kingdom was called Judah.
Israel was unfaithful to the
Lord and was taken into
captivity in 722 BC.

Exile
2 Kings 25,
2 Chronicles 36,
Esther,
Lamentations,
Ezekiel,
Daniel

The book of Lamentations
and the last chapters of
2 Kings and 2 Chronicles
describe the fall of
Jerusalem and the exile of
the people. The prophets
Daniel and Ezekiel were
taken into captivity by
Babylon. Esther describes
life in the Persian court.

Hardness
Malachi

Malachi prophesied about
one who would call the
nation to repentance
before the coming of the
Messiah.

Journeying with God

The Pentateuch

Introduction to the Pentateuch

The term *pentateuch* is Greek for "five scrolls." (A number of Old Testament books received Greek names when the Old Testament was translated into Greek in 70 BC.) The Pentateuch consists of the first five books of the Bible—Genesis, Exodus, Leviticus, Numbers, and Deuteronomy. The Jewish name for these five books is the Torah, or the Law. The Law is more than just the Ten Commandments and associated regulations; the Law traces the story of God's salvation, beginning with the creation of the universe and ending with God's people ready to go over the border into the Promised Land.

Beginning the Journey

The Pentateuch covers the first six eras of Old Testament history.

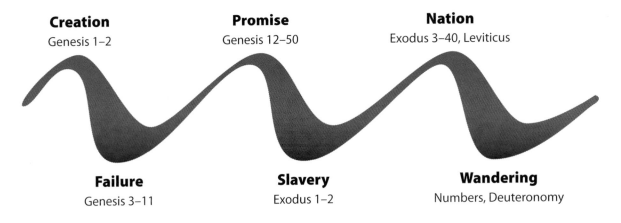

Creation
Genesis 1–2

Promise
Genesis 12–50

Nation
Exodus 3–40, Leviticus

Failure
Genesis 3–11

Slavery
Exodus 1–2

Wandering
Numbers, Deuteronomy

Authorship

Jews and Christians have generally recognized Moses as the author of the Pentateuch. The clearest statement of Moses' authorship is Deuteronomy 31:24–26: "After Moses finished writing in a book the words of this law from beginning to end, he gave this command to the Levites who carried the ark of the covenant of the Lord: 'Take this Book of the Law and place it beside the ark of the covenant of the Lord your God. There it will remain as a witness against you.'"

Middle East Region

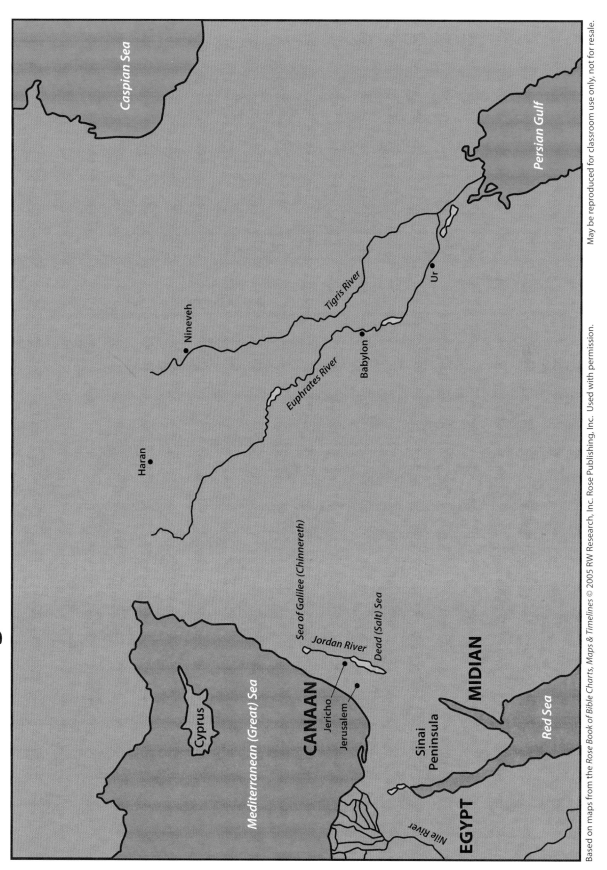

The major events in the Pentateuch took place in this area.

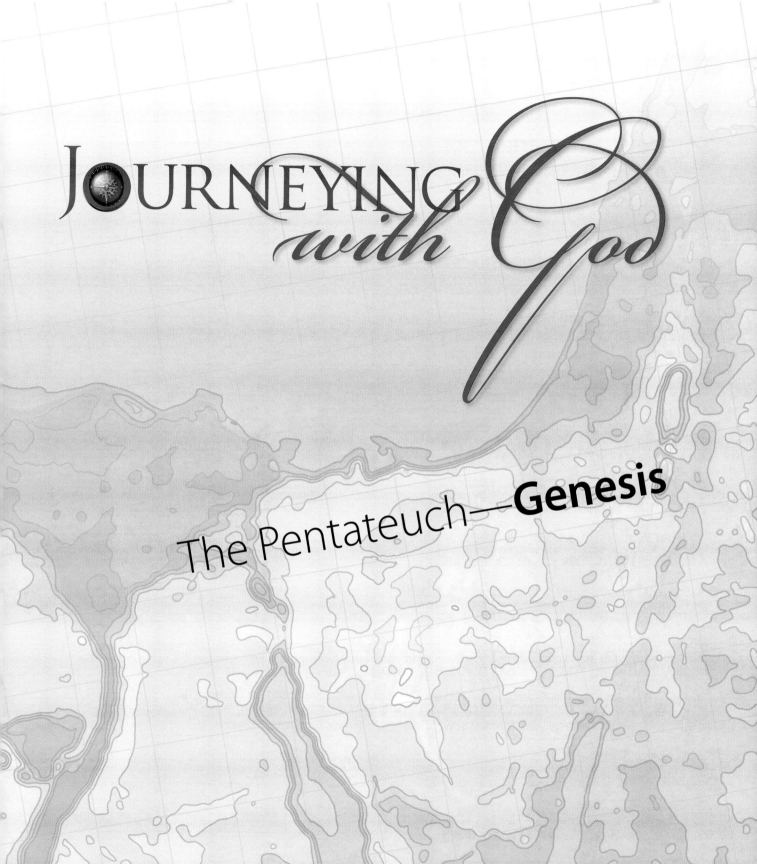

Journeying with God

The Pentateuch—Genesis

Genesis

Key Landmarks

Suggested Reading: Genesis 1–3, 6, 11, 12, 37, 49–50

Overview

Genesis is the Greek word for "beginning." Genesis is a foundational book for the rest of the Bible. It contains the first three eras of Old Testament history: Creation (1–2), Failure (3–11), and Promise (12–50).

Authorship and Date

Moses wrote Genesis while leading the people of Israel in the wilderness (1446–1406 BC). The book begins with Creation and ends with Jacob's family moving to Egypt (1876 BC).

Message: *Beginning of creation and the nation of Israel.*
Genesis records the beginning of the universe and of God's chosen people.

Taking the Journey

Creation

Promise

Nation

Failure

Slavery

Wandering

Finding Our Way

1. From Genesis 1, complete the chart by writing what God created on each day.

Formation: Replacing formlessness	Filling: Replacing the void
Day 1:	Day 4:
Day 2:	Day 5:
Day 3:	Day 6:

2. Compare God's commands to Adam in 1:28–30 with those to Noah in 9:1–7. What was similar?

What was different?

3. Following the birth of Seth and his son Enosh, what was people's response to God (4:26)?

In light of chapters 5 and 6, why was this response significant?

4. From Genesis, list at least two pairs of brothers in which a younger son was chosen rather than the firstborn.

5. The table of nations traces the families of what man's sons (10)?

6. Who are the main characters of Genesis 3:1–7?

Of 3:8–24?

7. Compare the way Satan tempted Adam and Eve (3:1–6) with the way he tempts people today. What are the similarities?

8. How does the Bible describe Noah's character? (Genesis 6:22, 7:1, 5; 8:20, Hebrews 11:7)

9. What promises did God make to Abram in Genesis 12:1–3?

10. What character traits do you find in Joseph?

11. Which sons of Jacob received the longest and greatest blessings? (49)

12. Pick one of the following people from Genesis: Adam, Eve, Noah, Abraham, Sarah, Isaac, Rebekah, Jacob, Rachel, Judah, or Joseph. Read what Genesis has to say about that person. Identify a specific sin in that person's life. Then answer this question: How did God in His grace use this person in spite of his or her sin?

13. What peaks and valleys are covered in the book of Genesis?

JOURNEYING with God

The Pentateuch—**Exodus**

Exodus

Key Landmarks

Suggested Reading: Exodus 1–3, 7–12, 20, 24, 39:32–40:38

Overview
The book of Exodus starts in the valley era of Slavery (Exodus 1–2) and then climbs to the mountaintop era of Nation.

Authorship and Date
Moses is the author. Exodus begins with Israel's redemption from Egypt and ends with the completion of the tabernacle (1446 BC).

Message: *God establishes Israel as His chosen nation.*
God's promises are fulfilled as God redeems Israel from Egypt, establishes the covenant at Sinai, and inhabits the tabernacle.

Taking the Journey

Creation   Promise   **Nation**

Failure   **Slavery**   Wandering

Finding Our Way

1. Why did the pharaoh enslave the Hebrews (1:8–10)?

2. What excuses did Moses give to God in trying to avoid leading Israel (3:11–4:17)?

3. What were the purposes for the plagues (7–11)?

4. Why were the Israelites commanded to celebrate the Passover feast (12)? What significance does the Passover have in the New Testament?

5. List the miracles that God performed during the Red Sea crossing (14:15–31).

6. According to Exodus 15, how long did the Israelites travel after the Red Sea crossing before they began to complain?

7. What three phrases did God use to describe what the Israelites would become if they kept the covenant (19:5–6)?

8. List the Ten Commandments. Which ones focus on a relationship to God?

Which ones focus on a relationship to other people?

9. What commandments did the Israelites break in Exodus 32? Why do you think this was such a serious offense?

10. What did God say about His character after Israel's golden-calf sin (Exodus 34:5–7)?

11. How did the Israelites know that God had accepted the tabernacle they had built (40)? Why do you think this event forms a fitting end to the book of Exodus?

12. According to Exodus 40, how did the Israelites know when it was time to pick up camp and continue on their journey?

13. After scanning Exodus 25–31, read Hebrews 8:1–10:18. Compare and contrast the work of the earthly tabernacle with the work of Christ.

14. What peaks and valleys are covered in the book of Exodus?

Journeying with God

The Pentateuch—Leviticus

Leviticus

Key Landmarks

Suggested Reading: Leviticus 1–7, 16–17, 19

Overview
The tabernacle represented God's presence in the midst of Israel. It was the place where the Israelites worshipped God through sacrifices. Leviticus describes the sacrificial system that was used in the tabernacle.

Authorship and Date
Moses wrote Leviticus. The book records the revelation given to him at Mt. Sinai (25:1–2, 26:46, 27:34). This would date the book around 1445–1444 BC.

Message: *A chosen nation relates to a holy God.*
Leviticus contains instructions to enable Israel to relate to the Lord, who is holy. The concept of holiness is referred to eighty-seven times in the book through detailed distinctions between holy and profane and between clean and unclean. Leviticus also contains instructions for restoring people's relationship with the Lord after sinning.

Taking the Journey

Finding Our Way

1. List and describe the five types of sacrifices prescribed in chapters 1–7 by filling in the chart below.

Name of the Offering	Object Offered	Manner of Sacrifice	Role of Blood in the Offering	Purpose of the Offering

2. Since all believers are priests (see 1 Peter 2:9), what lessons might be learned from God's instructions to the priests in Leviticus 8–10?

3. Compare the ministry of Aaron (Leviticus 16) and the ministry of Christ (Hebrews 9).

4. What do you think are some implications of the statement "the life … is in the blood"? (17:11)

5. Compare the specific commands of Leviticus 19 with the Ten Commandments (Exodus 20:2–17).

6. What are the observances in Leviticus 23? Why do you think God commanded these different observances?

7. What peaks and valleys are covered by the book of Leviticus?

Journeying with God

The Pentateuch—**Numbers**

Numbers

Key Landmarks

Suggested Reading: Numbers 13–14

Overview
The book of Numbers chronicles the rebellions of the generation that left Egypt.

Authorship and Date
Moses wrote Numbers (see Introduction to the Pentateuch). Numbers covers most of the period of Israel's journey from Egypt to the Promised Land. This would place this book's recorded history between 1446 and 1406 BC.

Message: *God replaces the rebelling exodus generation with a new generation.*
Numbers traces the failures of the exodus generation and prepares the new generation for life in the land.

Taking the Journey

Creation   Promise   Nation

Failure   Slavery   **Wandering**

Finding Our Way

1. What is the numerical difference between the total number of fighting men in the first census in Numbers (2:32) and the total number of fighting men in second census (26:51)?

2. How many died because of the rebellion of Israel in chapter 14?

3. Summarize the New Testament perspective on the rebellions in Numbers (Hebrews 3–4; 1 Corinthians 10:1–13). Why is the book of Numbers important for Christians today?

4. Using a concordance, find the New Testament passage that refers to the snake that Moses lifted up on a pole in the wilderness (21:4–9). What does the New Testament compare the serpent to?

5. What peaks and valleys are covered in the book of Numbers?

Journeying with God

The Pentateuch—**Deuteronomy**

Deuteronomy

Key Landmarks

Suggested Reading: Deuteronomy 6–8, 28

Overview
Numbers traces the replacing of the unbelieving exodus generation with the conquest generation. Deuteronomy records three major speeches from Moses to this second generation to prepare them to live in the land. The word *deuteronomy* comes from the Greek word for "second law."

Authorship and Date
Moses spoke and evidently recorded almost all of Deuteronomy in the fortieth and final year of wandering, when the Israelites were camped just across the Jordan River from the Promised Land (1:1–5). This fact places the speeches of Deuteronomy in 1405 BC.

Message: *A second law prepares a new generation for the Promised Land.*
Deuteronomy represents the final words of Moses to the conquest generation. Moses calls on the new generation to learn from their parents' unbelief and to follow the Lord wholeheartedly so that they will be able to possess the land and dwell there in obedience and prosperity for generations to come.

Taking the Journey

Creation   Promise   Nation

Failure   Slavery   **Wandering**

Finding Our Way

1. Why did Moses preach three long sermons to the people as they were preparing to enter the Promised Land?

2. List some of the topics of Moses' first sermon (1–4).

3. What are some of the commands that Moses gave in his second sermon (5–26)?

4. What were some of the blessings and curses in Moses' third sermon (27–28)?

5. How would you describe the theme of Moses' song (32)?

6. Why was Moses not allowed to enter the Promised Land (1, 3, 32)?

7. Compare God's love for Israel with God's love for us (7:7–13).

8. Read about the new covenant in Jeremiah 31:31–37. Compare the new covenant with the covenant found in Exodus and Deuteronomy.

9. What peaks and valleys are covered in the book of Deuteronomy?

Journeying with God

The Books of History

Introduction to the Books of History

The first book of history, Joshua, describes the conquest of the land; the last one, Esther, describes events that took place in Persia after some of the Jews had returned from exile. The books of history cover seven peaks and valleys of Old Testament history.

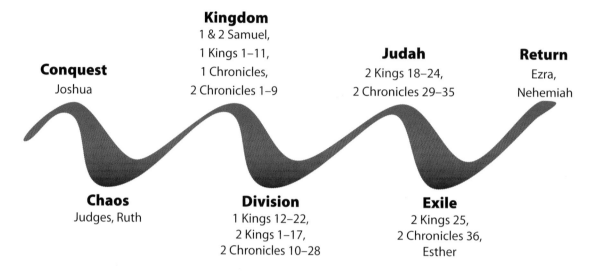

Kingdom
1 & 2 Samuel,
1 Kings 1–11,
1 Chronicles,
2 Chronicles 1–9

Conquest
Joshua

Judah
2 Kings 18–24,
2 Chronicles 29–35

Return
Ezra,
Nehemiah

Chaos
Judges, Ruth

Division
1 Kings 12–22,
2 Kings 1–17,
2 Chronicles 10–28

Exile
2 Kings 25,
2 Chronicles 36,
Esther

Continuing the Journey

The chart below shows how individual historical books are linked to the peaks and the valleys of the historical books.

Historical Era	Historical Books
Conquest	Joshua
Chaos	Judges, Ruth
Kingdom	1 and 2 Samuel, 1 Kings 1–11, 1 Chronicles, 2 Chronicles 1–9
Division	1 Kings 12–22, 2 Kings 1–17, 2 Chronicles 10–28
Judah	2 Kings 18–24, 2 Chronicles 29–35
Exile	2 Kings 25, 2 Chronicles 36, Esther
Return	Ezra, Nehemiah

Holy Land United

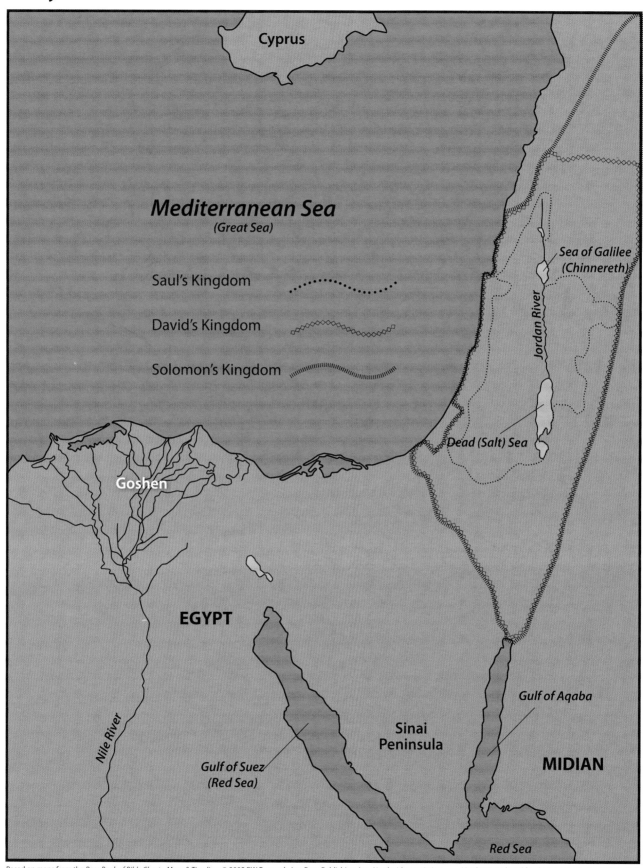

Cyprus

Mediterranean Sea
(Great Sea)

Saul's Kingdom

David's Kingdom

Solomon's Kingdom

Sea of Galilee
(Chinnereth)

Jordan River

Dead (Salt) Sea

Goshen

EGYPT

Nile River

Gulf of Suez
(Red Sea)

Sinai
Peninsula

Gulf of Aqaba

MIDIAN

Red Sea

Holy Land Divided

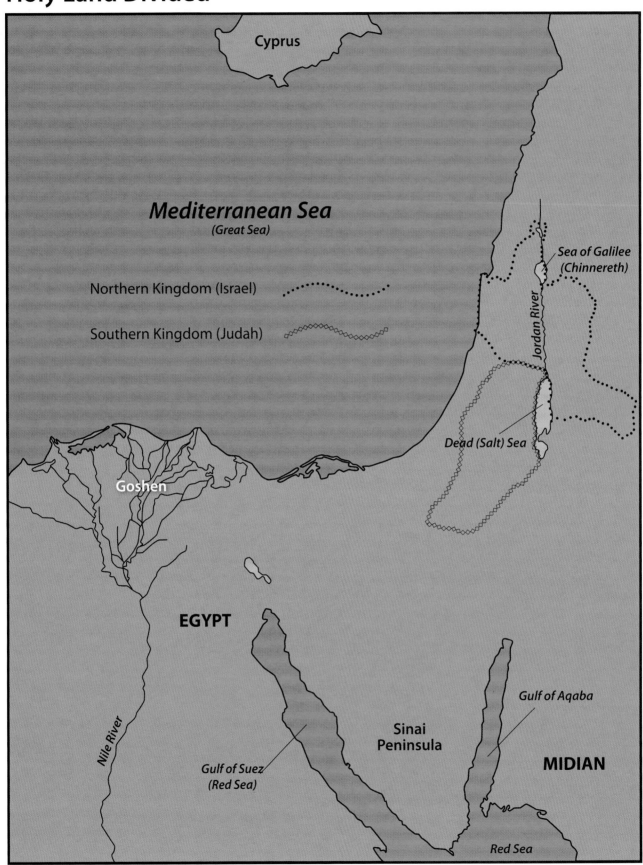

Cyprus

Mediterranean Sea
(Great Sea)

Northern Kingdom (Israel)

Southern Kingdom (Judah)

Sea of Galilee
(Chinnereth)

Jordan River

Dead (Salt) Sea

Goshen

EGYPT

Nile River

*Gulf of Suez
(Red Sea)*

Sinai
Peninsula

Gulf of Aqaba

MIDIAN

Red Sea

Journeying with God

The Books of History—Joshua

Joshua

Key Landmarks

Suggested Reading: Joshua 1, 6, 23–24

Overview

The book of Joshua records one of the great mountaintops of Israel's history. Through the second generation of Israelites after the exodus from Egypt, God fulfills His promise to give His people the land. The book contains such memorable stories as the battle at Jericho (6), the sin of Achan (7), the sun standing still (10), and other key events that allowed Israel to conquer the land of Canaan. The name *Joshua* means "the Lord saves."

Authorship and Date

The book itself does not name an author, nor is an author assigned to it anywhere else in Scripture. However, internal and external evidence suggests that Joshua and his contemporaries composed the bulk of the narrative, although some later editorial activity may have taken place. Thus the composition date is probably soon after the completion of the conquest, around 1400 BC.

Message: *The chosen nation conquers and divides the Promised Land.*
As the Israelites obey God, He enables them to conquer the inhabitants of the land. The land is then divided among the twelve tribes.

Taking the Journey

Conquest　　Kingdom　　Judah　　Return

Wandering　　Chaos　　Division　　Exile

Finding Our Way

1. Why did God punish the Canaanites through the conquest of the land? (See Genesis 15:16 and Deuteronomy 18:9–12.)

2. What does *Joshua* mean?

3. Where in the New Testament is Rahab mentioned? How is she portrayed?

4. What do the consequences of Achan's sin (7) teach us?

5. What were Joshua and Israel required to do in order to succeed in the conquest of the land (1:7–8)?

6. Why did Caleb receive a special inheritance from the Lord (14:6–15)?

7. What personal lessons may be learned from Joshua's life (24:1–27)?

8. What was the significance of recording the burial of Joseph's bones (24:32; Genesis 50:24–25)?

9. What peaks and valleys are covered in the book of Joshua?

Journeying with God

The Books of History—**Judges**

Judges

Key Landmarks

Suggested Reading: Judges 1–7

Overview

The book of Joshua leaves a lingering question about whether individual tribes of Israel would complete the job of driving out the Canaanites from the Promised Land. Judges opens with the disappointing answer that Israel did not completely obey God by possessing all the land. This incomplete obedience leads to a series of cycles that spiral down into spiritual chaos.

Authorship and Date

The book of Judges nowhere specifically identifies an author. However, internal and external clues place the composition date between the beginning of Saul's reign in 1051 BC and David's capture of Jerusalem in 1004 BC. The Talmud ascribes Judges to the hand of Samuel. Designating Samuel as the author certainly fits the above chronology, and he is noted as a writer (1 Samuel 10:25). If he is the author, he would have been writing to the generation under Saul's reign.

Message: *Incomplete possession of the land brings cycles of sin and judgment.*
Two phrases summarize the book of Judges: "there was no king in Israel" and "everyone did what was right in his own eyes" (21:25, NASB). The failure to possess the Promised Land completely and a lack of covenant loyalty lead to a downward spiritual spiral in a series of cycles; each cycle has three stages: disobedience, discipline, and deliverance.

Taking the Journey

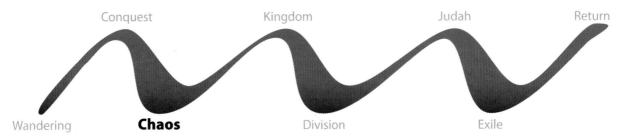

Conquest   Kingdom   Judah   Return

Wandering   **Chaos**   Division   Exile

Finding Our Way

1. Give one specific example of the three-part cycle—disobedience, discipline, deliverance—in the book of Judges.

2. What are the key factors in Israel's failure in Judges (2:10–31)?

3. Gideon seemed to be seeking God's will through the fleece, but what do you think was the real reason he put out the fleece (6:36–40)?

4. What were the main elements of the Nazirite vow (13:5; Numbers 6:1–8)? How did Samson break the vow?

5. Why does the author of Judges conclude the story of Dan's idolatry with the phrase "all the time the house of God was in Shiloh" (18:31)?

6. How do you think the last verse of Judges summarizes the message of the book and prepares us for later books?

7. What peaks and valleys are covered in the book of Judges?

JOURNEYING with God

The Books of History—Ruth

Ruth

Key Landmarks

Suggested Reading: Ruth 1–4

Overview
The events in the book of Ruth occurred during the period of the judges (1:1). In this deep valley of chaos, the book of Ruth provides a piercing ray of hope. Though the nation's faith waffled, faithful individuals within the nation continued to stay true to the Lord.

Authorship and Date
The book itself assigns no author. The Talmud attributes it to Samuel. The book was probably written during the reign of either David or Solomon by an anonymous author.

Message: *Love and loyalty lead to a royal line.*
Ruth records the beautiful love story of a widowed Moabite woman, Ruth, who expresses loyalty to her Israelite mother-in-law and to the Lord. Ruth remarries, and her son becomes a link in the royal line of David.

Taking the Journey

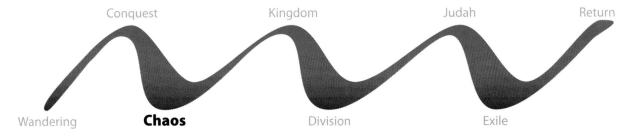

Conquest   Kingdom   Judah   Return

Wandering   **Chaos**   Division   Exile

Finding Our Way

1. What were the responsibilities of a kinsman-redeemer? (See Leviticus 25:25–28, 47–49; Deuteronomy 25:5–10.)

2. What purposes for Ruth do the beginning and ending of the book reveal?

3. Compare and contrast the lives of Boaz, Ruth, and Naomi with the lives of the majority of the Israelites, as recorded in the book of Judges.

4. Compare the feelings and actions of Naomi in 1:19–22 with her feelings and actions in 4:13–17.

5. What can be learned from Ruth's example in 1:14–18?

6. What peaks and valleys are covered in the book of Ruth?

Journeying with God

The Books of History—1 Samuel

1 Samuel

Key Landmarks

Suggested Reading: 1 Samuel 1–2, 8–9, 15–16

Overview

The book of 1 Samuel records the bumpy road to the peak of Israel's history following the spiritual decline of Israel in the book of Judges. The book captures this transition from the chaos of the time of the judges through the tragic reign of Saul to the choosing of Israel's greatest king, David.

Authorship and Date

The Talmud assigns 1 Samuel 1–24 to Samuel and the remainder of 1 Samuel and all of 2 Samuel to Nathan and Gad. The books themselves do not name an author. The books of 1 and 2 Samuel must have been composed after David's death (2 Samuel 23:1); therefore, they were written sometime after 970 BC. The books of Samuel cover the period of Israel's history from the end of the judges period through the death of David, approximately 1080–970 BC.

Message: *Saul provides a tragic transition from wicked judges to godly David.*
The book of 1 Samuel traces the transition from a failed theocracy (direct rule of God) in the time of the judges to a godly monarchy under David. Israel is rejecting the Lord, and the Israelites' disobedience, not their lack of a king, is the root cause of Israel's troubles. The disobedient leaders (Eli and Saul) are replaced by the obedient ones (Samuel and David).

Taking the Journey

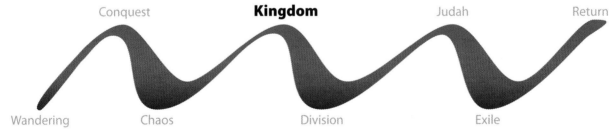

Conquest **Kingdom** Judah Return

Wandering Chaos Division Exile

Finding Our Way

1. From 1 Samuel 1, describe the family into which Samuel was born.

2. How does 3:19–4:1 describe Samuel's ministry as a prophet?

3. What does the story of the lost and returned ark teach (4:1–7:2)?

4. a. Why did the Israelites say they wanted a king (8:4–5, 19–20)?

   b. What was the real reason behind Israel's desire for a king (8:6–8)?

c. What did Samuel warn would happen if they chose a king (8:11–18)?

5. What were the main reasons God took the kingdom away from Saul (15:22–26)?

6. Why didn't David take Saul's life, even though he had more than one chance (24, 26)?

7. What peaks and valleys are covered in the book of 1 Samuel?

Journeying with God

The Books of History—2 Samuel

2 Samuel

Key Landmarks

Suggested Reading: 2 Samuel 1, 7, 11–12, 22

Overview
The book of 2 Samuel continues the climb to the pinnacle of Israel's history in the Kingdom era. In 1 Samuel, God chooses David to be king; in 2 Samuel, God establishes David on the throne.

Authorship and Date
See the corresponding section under 1 Samuel for authorship. The book of 2 Samuel focuses on the reign of David (1011–971 BC).

Message: *God rules Israel through the king who is after His own heart.*
The book of 1 Samuel records the initiation of a godly monarchy under David; 2 Samuel continues that account as God establishes the Davidic throne. The continuation of David's line is based on the covenant of the Lord, despite the failures of David and his household.

Taking the Journey

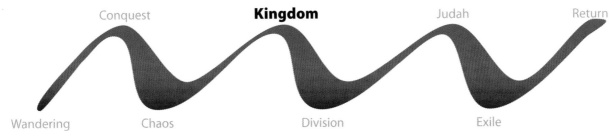

Finding Our Way

1. After hearing Nathan's parable, David said that the rich man of the parable should pay fourfold (12:6). What four calamities fell on David's household as recorded in the rest of 2 Samuel?

2. Briefly tell how David described Saul and Jonathan in his lament after their death (1:17–27). What is surprising about these descriptions?

3. Why is the promise of 2 Samuel 7:15 so important in light of the events in the previous book?

4. What are the two ways the term *house* is used in 2 Samuel 7:5–13?

5. What are the basic promises of the Davidic covenant? (7:12–16)

6. What lessons may be learned from David's sin and repentance in 2 Samuel 11–12?

7. What peaks and valleys are covered in the book of 2 Samuel?

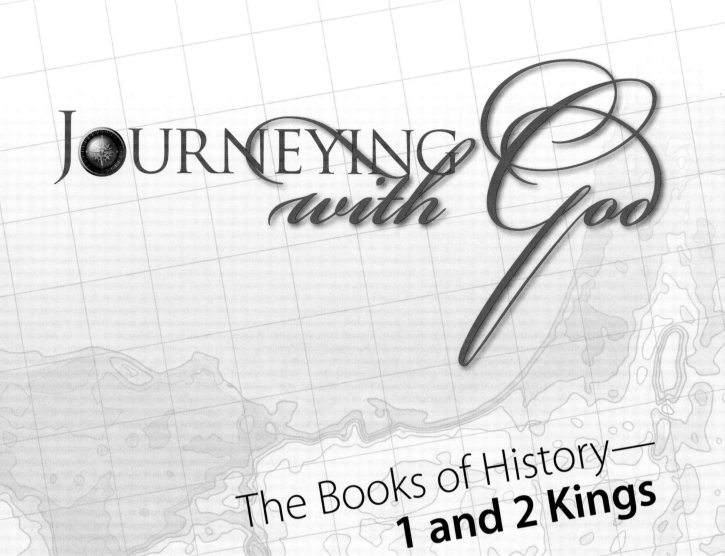

Journeying with God

The Books of History— 1 and 2 Kings

1 and 2 Kings

Key Landmarks

Suggested Reading: 1 Kings 6, 8, 11–12, 17–22; 2 Kings 2, 17, 18, 25

Overview

The book of 1 Kings begins with the reign of Solomon during the peak of Israel's power. It then records Solomon's fall and the subsequent division of the kingdom into two nations: the northern kingdom of Israel and the southern kingdom of Judah. The book of 2 Kings continues the sad spiritual story as it records the fall of both nations. The bright spots are found in the reforming kings of Judah and in the rise of the prophetic office, founded by Elijah and Elisha.

Authorship and Date

The Hebrew Bible combines 1 and 2 Kings into a single unit. The Septuagint (the 70 BC Greek translation of the Old Testament) divided them into two books because the large scroll of the Kings needed to be divided into two smaller scrolls of near equal length.

Though the text gives evidence of a single author, the author's identity is unknown. The author must have written after 560 BC, since the release of Jehoiachin is mentioned (2 Kings 25:27). The books must have been written before the return of the Jews in 538 BC, since the author certainly would have included such a momentous event.

Message: *God's rule in Israel is hampered by a divided heart and a divided kingdom.*
The books of the Kings present covenantal faithfulness as the measure of Judah's and Israel's kings, the message of the prophets, and the mark of the Lord. The faithfulness of the kings is judged primarily by their obedient worship. The prophets emphasize the requirement of obedience to the sure word of the Lord. God demonstrates His covenantal faithfulness through the preservation of a Davidic line and through His blessings on the obedient.

Taking the Journey

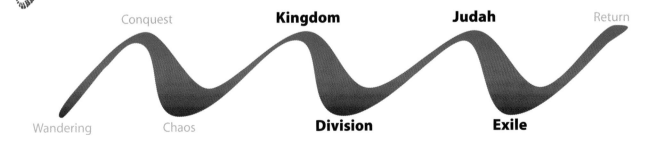

 **Finding Our Way**

1. How did Solomon demonstrate his devotion to the Lord?

2. How did Solomon drift away from the Lord?

3. Why did the kingdom split after Solomon's death?

4. Who was the first ruler of the northern kingdom? Who was the first ruler of the southern kingdom?

5. Choose one of the godly kings of Judah (Asa, Jehoshaphat, Joash, Amaziah, Uzziah, Jotham, Hezekiah, Josiah) and answer these questions about him:
  a. How did he show that he followed the Lord?
  b. How thoroughly did he eradicate idol worship?
  c. Who was his predecessor? Was he faithful to the Lord?
  d. Who was his successor? Was he faithful to the Lord?
  e. Did he remain faithful to God?

6. What countries carried the two kingdoms (Israel and Judah) into captivity (2 Kings 17, 25)?

7. What peaks and valleys are covered in the books of 1 and 2 Kings?

Journeying with God

The Books of History—
1 and 2 Chronicles

1 and 2 Chronicles

Key Landmarks

Suggested Reading: 1 Chronicles 17, 21–22; 2 Chronicles 5–8, 36

Overview
The books of 1 and 2 Chronicles cover essentially the same historical eras as do the books of Samuel and Kings, but with different emphases. Samuel and Kings place more emphasis on military and political history, while Chronicles captures more of the priestly emphasis. Thus, the temple and the kings who reformed Judah's worship have larger roles in Chronicles.

Authorship and Date
The books of 1 and 2 Chronicles do not specify an author. The Talmud names Ezra as the chronicler, and internal pointers make Ezra a plausible choice. Most conservative scholars place the composition of the books around 450–400 BC.

Message: *Priestly editorial on King David and Judah's reforming kings.*
The book of 1 Chronicles, written to a Return-era audience, reinforces the people's relationship to historic Israel and to its beloved King David, establishes the importance of righteous worship at the temple, and reiterates the enduring covenant of the Lord with David. The book of 2 Chronicles continues the narrative begun in 1 Chronicles.

Taking the Journey

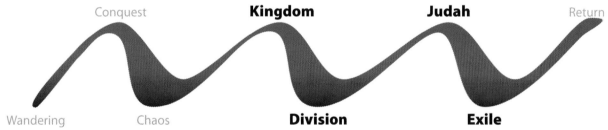

Conquest   **Kingdom**   **Judah**   Return

Wandering   Chaos   **Division**   **Exile**

Finding Our Way

1. Name three kings of Judah who followed the Lord (partially or completely). Name three who did not.

2. What reason did God give for allowing the people of Judah to be taken into captivity?

3. What peaks and valleys are covered in the books of 1 and 2 Chronicles?

Journeying with God

The Books of History—**Ezra**

Ezra

Key Landmarks

Suggested Reading: Ezra 1, 4–6, 9–10

Overview
The book of Ezra records key events of the Return era, including spiritual reforms and the rebuilding of the temple.

Authorship and Date
The book does not directly specify its author. It does, however, imply Ezra's authorship through the use of the first person in 7:27–9:15. Ezra, as a priest and a scribe (7:21), certainly had the qualifications to be the author. The Talmud also names Ezra as the author (*Baba Bathra* 15a). There seems to be no strong reason to ascribe the authorship to anyone else.

Message: *Rebuilding of the temple and revival of the people.*
Ezra provides a historical account of the reconstruction of the temple (1–6) and then gives a personal account of the spiritual revival of the Jews, especially their separation from the pagan people of the land (7–10).

Taking the Journey

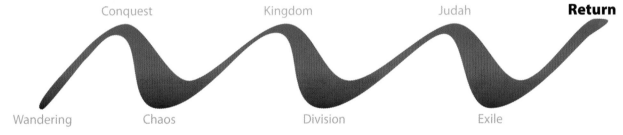

Conquest   Kingdom   Judah   **Return**

Wandering   Chaos   Division   Exile

Finding Our Way

1. Why were the mixed marriages such a threat to the returnees in Ezra (9)?

2. Why do you think Ezra 7:10 is such an important statement about Ezra?

3. Describe some key leadership qualities Ezra exhibited throughout the book.

4. What peaks and valleys are covered in the book of Ezra?

Journeying with God

The Books of History—Nehemiah

Nehemiah

Key Landmarks

Suggested Reading: Nehemiah 1–2, 6, 12:27–13:31

Overview
Nehemiah records key events of the Return era. Nehemiah traces the rebuilding of the broken walls of Jerusalem and the instituting of social reforms.

Authorship and Date
The book opens with the phrase "The words of Nehemiah" (1:1), indicating that at least the beginning section was composed originally by Nehemiah. However, in the oldest Hebrew Bibles, Ezra and Nehemiah are only one book. This fact leads some scholars to suggest that Ezra, using Nehemiah's memoirs for large sections (1:1–7:5, 12:27–43, 13:4–31), wrote the book of Nehemiah. It appears that these memoirs were used to compose a single work that is now divided in our Bibles as the books of Ezra and Nehemiah.

Message: *Rebuilding of the wall and reform of the people.*
First, the book of Nehemiah records the grace of the Lord in providing for the rebuilding of the broken walls of Jerusalem. Second, it traces the spiritual reformation required and experienced among the returnees to Jerusalem.

Taking the Journey

Finding Our Way

1. Outline and analyze the response of Nehemiah to Jerusalem's trouble in chapter 1. Develop an outline of his response and describe parts that set an example for us today.

2. Summarize what the book of Nehemiah teaches about prayer. Key references include 1:4–11, 2:4, 4:4–5, 9, 5:19, 6:9, 14, 13:14, 22, 29, and 31.

3. List the reforms Nehemiah pursued (13). Why do you think these reforms might be important to the remnant living in Jerusalem?

4. What peaks and valleys are covered by the book of Nehemiah?

Journeying with God

The Books of History—**Esther**

Esther

Key Landmarks

Suggested Reading: Esther 1–10

Overview
While Ezra and Nehemiah chronicle the work of the return to Jerusalem, Esther records God's protection of those exiled Jews who did not return to the Promised Land.

Authorship and Date
The internal evidence points to authorship by a Persian Jew, but contradictory external evidence prevents one from naming a specific author. The date of composition is hinted at in the text. It seems to be after 465 BC, which was when the reign of Xerxes (Hebrew name, Ahasuerus) ended.

Message: *God anonymously uses a Persian queen to preserve His people on Purim.*
Though the name of God is not mentioned in the book, Esther is a beautifully written story of the providence of the Lord in preserving and exalting His people. He works completely behind the scenes through obedient servants such as Esther and Mordecai. The book also demonstrates that God is able to reverse the fortunes of those He has chosen.

Taking the Journey

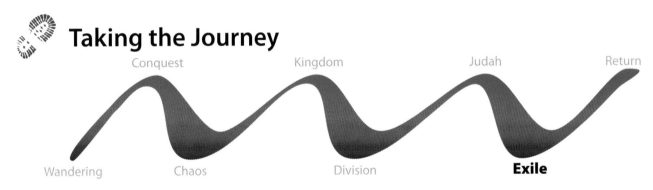

Conquest   Kingdom   Judah   Return

Wandering   Chaos   Division   **Exile**

Finding Our Way

1. What very important character is never mentioned in Esther? Why do you think this person's name is missing?

2. List the different ways God worked behind the scenes to save Esther and the Jews. In what ways does God work behind the scenes in our lives as well?

3. What peaks and valleys are covered by the book of Esther?

Journeying with God

The Poetic Books

Introduction to the Poetic Books

The poetic books represent the wisdom and poetry writings of the Israelites. The works of wisdom include the practical sayings of Proverbs, the deep reflections of Job and Ecclesiastes, and the poetic imagery of Song of Songs. The book of Psalms, the hymnbook of Israel, expresses the greatest fears and the highest hopes of God's people in worship.

It is not possible to put the poetic books neatly into specific eras. For example, though the events in the book of Job may have happened in the era of Promise, it probably wasn't put into writing until the Kingdom era. Though about half the psalms were written in the Kingdom era, the book of Psalms contains a psalm written by Moses and several written during or after the Exile era. However, since such a great amount of poetry and wisdom literature was written and compiled during the Kingdom era, we have placed all these books within that era for the purposes of this course.

Kingdom
Job, Psalms, Proverbs, Ecclesiastes, Song of Songs

Chaos

Hebrew Poetry

More than one-third of the Old Testament was written in poetic form. The poetic books are Job, Psalms, Proverbs, Ecclesiastes, and Song of Songs. Poetry can also be found in many parts of narrative and prophetic books.

Narrative and didactic writing communicate history and logic well, but poetry conveys emotion. The poetic books and the prophetic books contain much poetry because their messages evoke powerful emotions.

Parallelism
The primary poetic device of Hebrew poetry is parallelism. In parallelism, one verse or one line is linked to another in specific ways.

Synonymous parallelism. The second line repeats the thought of the first line in different words.

Psalm 2:1:
Why do the nations conspire
and the peoples plot in vain?

Psalm 148:1:
Praise the Lord from the heavens,
praise him in the heights above.

Synthetic parallelism. The second line (sometimes the next several lines) develops the thought introduced in the first line.

Psalm 1:1:
Blessed is the man
who does not walk in the counsel of the
    wicked
or stand in the way of sinners
or sit in the seat of mockers.

Psalm 1:2:
But his delight is in the law of the Lord,
and on his law he meditates day and night.

Psalm 95:3:
For the Lord is the great God,
the great King above all gods.

Emblematic parallelism. One line contains the main thought while the next line (or lines) describes the thought with a simile, a metaphor, or an image.

Psalm 103:13:
As a father has compassion on his children,
so the Lord has compassion on those who
    fear him.

Psalm 42:1:
As the deer pants for streams of water,
so my soul pants for you, O God.

Psalm 23:1–2:
The Lord is my shepherd, I shall not be in
    want.
He makes me lie down in green pastures.
he leads me beside quiet waters,
he restores my soul.

Antithetical parallelism. The next line (or lines) contrasts with the thought of the first line.

Psalm 1:6:
For the Lord watches over the way of the
    righteous,
but the way of the wicked will perish.

Psalm 11:5:
The Lord examines the righteous,
but the wicked and those who love violence
his soul hates.

Climactic parallelism. The second line repeats the first line with the addition of a word or words. The added term (or terms) becomes the main emphasis or climax.

Psalm 94:1:
O Lord, the God who avenges,
O God who avenges, shine forth.

Psalm 29:1:
Ascribe to the Lord, O mighty ones,
ascribe to the Lord glory and strength.

Other Features of Hebrew Poetry

In addition to parallelism, Hebrew poetry uses other important devices. These features aid interpretation and enhance the beauty of the poetry.

Refrain. The recurrence of a phrase or a line at regular intervals. Refrains often mark sections within a psalm. They resemble a chorus sung at the end of every verse of a hymn today.

Psalm 39:5, 11:
Each man's life is but a breath. Selah
. . . .
Each man is but a breath. Selah.

Inclusio. The use of a word, a phrase, or a line both at the beginning and the end of a section of a psalm to enclose a unit of thought. It could be called a literary parenthesis.

Psalm 8:1–9:
O Lord, our Lord,
how majestic is your name in all the earth!
. . . .
  . . .
O Lord, our Lord,
how majestic is your name in all the earth!

Psalm 22:1–10:
My God …
. . . .
… my God.

Acrostics. Each line or stanza begins with a sequential letter of the Hebrew alphabet. See Psalms 37 and 119 and Lamentations 3.

Journeying with God

The Poetic Books—**Job**

Job

Key Landmarks

Suggested Reading: Job 1–2, 5, 8, 11, 28, 33, 38–42

Overview

Job stands as a unique book in that it was likely written in the Kingdom era about events that occurred during the Promise era (the era of Abraham, Isaac, and Jacob). The book discusses an issue that is universal: human suffering and the sovereignty of God.

Authorship and Date

The identity of the author will probably never be known with certainty. The author is characterized by deep empathy for Job's suffering, education in wisdom tradition and literary devices, insight into the conventional wisdom of divine retribution, high standards for personal ethics, knowledge of nature, and knowledge of Promise-era place names. The most plausible explanation may be that the story of Job was passed down through oral tradition and then exquisitely recreated in the period of wisdom writing in Israel—the period that began with Solomon during the Kingdom era and continued through the reign of Hezekiah.

Message: *A suffering saint meets a sovereign God.* The message of Job may be summarized as follows: God is sovereignly free to act as He wills, despite human conceptions of Him, for the purpose of displaying His glory in the material and spiritual worlds. The disconnection between the faithfulness and the suffering of Job exemplifies God's sovereign prerogative and corrects the divine-retribution theology of his friends.

Taking the Journey

Conquest   **Kingdom**   Judah   Return

Wandering   Chaos   Division   Exile

Finding Our Way

1. The dialogue and monologue cycles in Job make up the vast majority of the book. To synthesize the views presented in the book of Job, read representative sections of each speaker's discourses and summarize each view. Summarize the key point(s) of each speaker and then cite verse references to demonstrate those points. Use the following chart:

Speaker	Summary of views
Eliphaz (4–5)	
Bildad (8)	
Zophar (11)	
Elihu (32–37)	

2. Study the main statements of Job to show how he changed through the course of the book. Summarize his statements in chapter 3, analyze his final monologue in chapter 31, and then compare those speeches with his responses after God speaks (40:3–5, 42:1–6).

3. Summarize how God answered Job in chapters 40–41. Why do you think God did not tell Job about the arrangement with Satan?

4. What peaks and valleys are covered in the book of Job?

Journeying with God

The Poetic Books—Psalms

Psalms

Key Landmarks

Suggested Reading: Your teacher will give you reading assignments.

Overview

About half of the psalms (73 of 150) are ascribed to David. These psalms and many others were composed during the Kingdom era. However, as noted below, the composition and compilation of the book of Psalms span about 1,000 years. Traditionally, the book of Psalms has been divided into five "books": Psalms 1–41, 42–72, 73–89, 90–106, and 107–150.

Authorship and Date

The book of Psalms is not the product of a single author but a compilation of works from a number of authors over the course of many centuries. The earliest known psalm in the psalter was written by Moses (Psalm 90); others were clearly composed by postexilic authors (126). Specified authors include David, Asaph (50, 73–83), Heman (88), Ethan (89) and Solomon (72, 127).

Scholars place most psalter editorial work during four periods. The first period was during the reign of David and shortly after his death. The second was during Jehoshaphat's rule. The third happened when Hezekiah revived temple worship. The fourth was during the postexilic time of Ezra. For the purposes of this course, the book of Psalms is placed in the Kingdom era.

Message: *Prayers and praises of God's people.* The book of Psalms captures the responses of the people of God to His awesome and gracious character. Some psalms exalt His greatness and power; some marvel at His mercy and kindness; some puzzle at His mystery and uniqueness. The bottom line is that God is the primary subject.

Literary Forms of Psalms

The form of a psalm is determined by examining its structure, content, vocabulary, and setting in comparison with similar psalms.

Psalms of lament. These psalms express grief and need, either of an individual or of Israel as

Taking the Journey

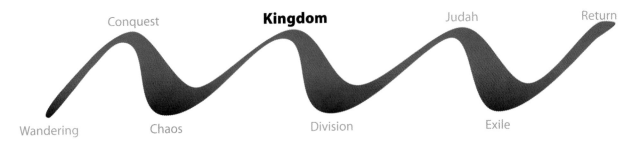

Conquest   **Kingdom**   Judah   Return

Wandering   Chaos   Division   Exile

a nation. Examples of individual laments: 3, 5, 6, 7, 17, 25, 27, 31, 38, 39, 56, 69, 88, and 140. Examples of national laments: 12, 44, 60, 74, 79, 80, 83, 85, and 126. A special category within lament psalms are the imprecatory psalms—psalms calling for divine judgment. Examples of imprecatory psalms: 7, 35, 58, 59, 69, 83, and 137.

Acknowledgement psalms. These psalms express specific praise of God's work for the psalmist. Examples include 30, 32, 34, 66, 116, and 138.

Descriptive praise psalms. These are psalms of general praise of the attributes of God, His character, and His work for His people. Examples: 19, 29, 33, 111, 113, 114, 135, 136, and 145–150.

Royal psalms. These psalms express praise for God's work in behalf of Israel's king. Examples include 2, 18, 20, 21, 45, 72, 89, 101, 110, and 144.

Enthronement psalms. These psalms praise God for His reign over the nations and the earth. Examples: 48, 93, and 96–99.

Psalms of ascent. These psalms were intended to be sung in preparation for annual festivals in Jerusalem. Examples: 42–43, 84, and 120–134.

Wisdom psalms. These psalms analyze ways of life and their consequences. Examples: 1, 14, 19, 49, 73, 112, 119, and 128.

Messianic psalms. A messianic psalm is one in which the Spirit guided the psalmist to write about Christ. Some psalms present a type of Christ. Examples include 69:8–9 (see John 2:17, 7:3–5) and 41:9 (see Matthew 26:14–16). In other psalms, the psalmist describes his own life in hyperbolic language so that the language is literally fulfilled in Christ's life. Examples are found in 22 (crucifixion) and 34:19–20 (see John 19:36). Some psalms describe Israel's king literally, but the psalm is ultimately fulfilled in Christ. For examples, see 2 and 72. One psalm refers to Christ alone and not to any other king or person. In Psalm 110, David records the Lord speaking to Messiah. Finally, some psalms focus on features of God's kingdom that will find ultimate fulfillment in Christ. Examples are Psalms 96–99.

Finding Our Way

1. Read any 15 psalms. Fill out this chart after reading each psalm. The last column asks for an application of the psalm. Think of times in your own life or in someone else's life when this psalm could have been helpful.

Psalm	Type of psalm	Theme or main subject	Application for today

2. On a separate sheet of paper, compose poems that use each of the types of parallelism as well as the other poetic devices used in Hebrew poetry. (See the introduction to the poetic books.) Label each poem with the poetic devices utilized.

3. What peaks and valleys are covered in the book of Psalms?

Journeying with God

The Poetic Books—**Proverbs**

Proverbs

Key Landmarks

Suggested Reading: Proverbs 1–2, 9, 31

Overview
The book of Proverbs rises out of the Kingdom era of Israel's history. Solomon is the primary author, ruling in the peak of the Kingdom era. The wise men of Hezekiah's reign later compiled more proverbs during the Judah period.

Authorship and Date
Proverbs is the product of several authors and editors. Contributors include Solomon (see 1:1, 10:1, 25:1), the men of Hezekiah (25:1), Agur (30:1), Lemuel (31:1), and "the wise" (22:17, 24:23, see 1 Kings 4:31).

The book was begun during the reign of Solomon (971–931 BC) and was probably completed during the reign of Hezekiah (729–686 BC).

Message: *The fear of the Lord produces wisdom.*

The key to the message of the book is found in the opening lines. The introduction delineates five purposes for Proverbs: (1) for understanding wisdom and discipline, (2) for understanding words of insight, (3) for acquiring words of insight, (4) for giving prudence to the simple, and (5) for understanding the words of the wise. These purposes dovetail with the overall message that encourages the reader to live a skillful life founded on the fear of Yahweh.

Taking the Journey

Finding Our Way

1. The main headings in Proverbs are found in 1:1, 10:1, 24:23, 25:1, 30:1, and 31:1. What do they tell about the book?

2. How do Proverbs 1:1–7 and 31:10–31 introduce and conclude the book? Compare and contrast what they say.

3. In your own words, define *wisdom* as it is used in Proverbs.

4. Follow the style used in Proverbs to compose contemporary proverbs on issues important to you.

5. Use a concordance to find the uses of the phrase "the fear of the Lord" in Proverbs. What does Proverbs teach about this important phrase?

6. What peaks and valleys are covered in the book of Proverbs?

Journeying with God

The Poetic Books—Ecclesiastes

Ecclesiastes

Key Landmarks

Suggested Reading: Ecclesiastes 1, 3, 11–12

Overview
The book of Ecclesiastes captures Solomon's wistful reflections about a life given to seeking satisfaction in all human pursuits.

Authorship and Date
The book leaves very few clues about its date of composition. The language of the book has provoked many debates and proposals, but no clear consensus has been achieved. Also, the vague historical references (4:13–14 and 9:14–15) have yielded little help in dating the book. The key issue in proposing a date is resolving its authorship. For the purposes of this course, we will assume that Ecclesiastes was composed by Solomon toward the end of his life as he reflected back over his accomplishments and their significance.

Message: *Enjoying God's incredible, mysterious gift of life.*

The Greek word *ecclesiastes* means "the teacher" or "the preacher." The book of Ecclesiastes is the complex verdict of a sage in search of the key to finding and understanding the significance of life. The message is seen in the desire of Solomon to find wisdom and enduring satisfaction in life (1:12–2:11) and in his wrestling with divine sovereignty (2:26, 3:14, 7:13–14, 8:16–9:1) in the face of the incongruities of life (8:14–17). The conclusion of his experiential and observational investigation is that life is an incomprehensible enigma to be enjoyed as a gift from the Creator and Judge. So Ecclesiastes is not pessimistic in outlook. The book recognizes the perplexing aspects of life while affirming faith in an all-wise and all-powerful God who has granted our lot in life. We are to enjoy that life as a gift of God, and we are to remember that our life will be judged by God.

Taking the Journey

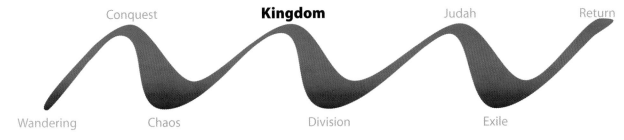

Conquest   **Kingdom**   Judah   Return

Wandering   Chaos   Division   Exile

Finding Our Way

1. Compare Ecclesiastes 1:2 and 12:8. These verses repeat a key phrase from the book and represent the introduction and a conclusion to the book. What is that phrase, and what does it mean?

2. Read the following passages and compile a summary of human pursuits: 2:15–16, 19–21, 26, 4:4, 8, 5:10, 6:9, 7:4, 8:10, 14.

3. What important lessons does 11:9–12:7 have for a teenager?

4. What peaks and valleys are covered in the book of Ecclesiastes?

Journeying with God

The Poetic Books—
Song of Songs

Song of Songs

Key Landmarks

Suggested Reading: Song of Songs 1–8

Overview
Song of Songs is a story of love, courtship, and marriage. It is presented as a musical poem with parts for Solomon, his beloved, and a chorus.

Authorship and Date
Traditionally, the authorship has been assigned to Solomon. Some scholars have challenged that view because of linguistic studies that seem to show late influences in the language.

One concern with Solomonic authorship is the problem of Solomon's 700 wives and 300 concubines (1 Kings 11:3). How could this man write of love and fidelity? One possibility is that the book is tied to Solomon's early life and the courtship with his first wife. The book was written during the Kingdom era, likely during the early stages of Solomon's rule, before the events of 1 Kings 11.

Message: *Exaltation of married love.*
As noted above, the book is a song that applauds pure human love. Its message is a divine endorsement of the chaste and full enjoyment of the emotional and sexual closeness granted to husband and wife. God Himself created man and woman and brought them together into intimate relationship. Song of Songs explores and extols the incredible physical and emotional joys of that intimate relationship. Also, since such a relationship so often provides the scriptural pattern of God's love, the book's overall message must include typological elements that look forward to the ultimate marriage between the Lord and His people in heaven.

Taking the Journey

Conquest   **Kingdom**   Judah   Return

Wandering   Chaos   Division   Exile

Finding Our Way

1. Describe or summarize the love relationship between Solomon and the Shulammite woman in this book.

2. After reading the Song of Songs, what impressions do you have about God's plan for romantic love?

3. What peaks and valleys are covered in the Song of Songs?

Journeying with God

The Books of Prophecy

Introduction to the Books of Prophecy

The prophetic office was founded by Elijah and Elisha. Later prophets, including those who wrote books, established their ministries on this foundation. God called prophets to be His voice at a time when kings could no longer be trusted to speak faithfully for God. The prophetic period begins with the Division era and continues through the Hardness era.

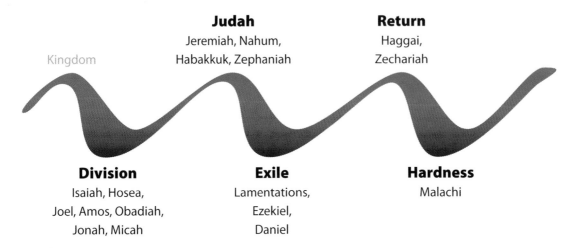

Judah
Jeremiah, Nahum, Habakkuk, Zephaniah

Return
Haggai, Zechariah

Kingdom

Division
Isaiah, Hosea, Joel, Amos, Obadiah, Jonah, Micah

Exile
Lamentations, Ezekiel, Daniel

Hardness
Malachi

Below is a chart showing the eras, the prophets, and the nations they ministered to.

Historical Era	Historical Books	Prophetic Books
Division	1 Kings 12–2 Kings 17 2 Chronicles 10–28	*To Israel:* Hosea, Amos *To other nations:* Obadiah, Jonah *To Judah:* Isaiah, Joel, Micah
Judah	2 Kings 18–24 2 Chronicles 29–35	Jeremiah, Nahum, Habakkuk, Zephaniah
Exile	2 Kings 25, 2 Chronicles 36, Esther	Lamentations, Ezekiel, Daniel
Return	Ezra, Nehemiah	Haggai, Zechariah
Hardness		Malachi

JOURNEYING with God

The Major Prophets

Introduction to the Major Prophets

The first five books of prophecy—Isaiah, Jeremiah, Lamentations, Ezekiel, and Daniel—are called the Major Prophets. The name refers to the length of the books. Though Lamentations is much shorter than some of the Minor Prophets, it is included among the Major Prophets because the book is associated with the prophet Jeremiah.

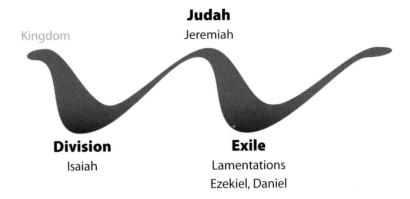

Kingdom

Judah
Jeremiah

Division
Isaiah

Exile
Lamentations
Ezekiel, Daniel

Journeying with God

The Major Prophets—Isaiah

Isaiah

Key Landmarks

Suggested Reading: 1, 6–9, 36–40, 52–53, 61, 66

Overview
Isaiah began prophesying to the southern kingdom, Judah, during the Division era—about twenty years before the northern kingdom, Israel, was taken into captivity.

Authorship and Date
The title of the book comes from the book itself, which claims Isaiah as its author (1:1, 2:1, 7:3, 13:1, 20:2, 37:2, 6, 21, 38:1, 4, 21, 39:3, 5). In the New Testament, Isaiah is mentioned twenty-one times as the author of the book. External evidence is equally convincing. Isaiah is the only author connected with the book in the ancient Hebrew manuscripts. Josephus (*Antiquities* 11.1.1–2) also held that Isaiah was the author.

Isaiah includes some historical pointers within his book that can help establish the date of writing. His ministry began with his call (6:1) after Uzziah's death (740 BC). His ministry spanned the reigns of Jotham, Ahaz, and Hezekiah and extended into Manasseh's wicked rule. Since Isaiah records the death of Sennacherib (37:38), he must have ministered until 680 or 681 BC.

Message: *Trust only in God, who brings judgment and salvation.*
Isaiah, prophesying to the deafened ears and hardened hearts of Judah in the late eighth century BC, calls on the nation to cease from its wickedness and from seeking help from foreign nations and to turn instead to the Lord, who alone will protect and deliver His people through His Servant and bring them all His promised blessings.

Taking the Journey

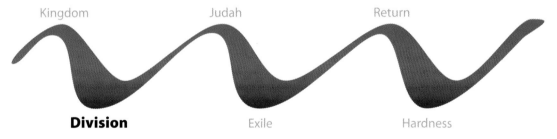

Kingdom   Judah   Return

Division   Exile   Hardness

 # Finding Our Way

1. What kings of Judah reigned while Isaiah was prophesying?

2. What two foreign world powers are featured in Isaiah 36–39? What is their significance?

3. Using the following Isaiah passages, summarize what Isaiah teaches concerning Christ's ministry:

Prophecy	Fulfillment in Jesus
7:10–14	
9:2–7	
11:1–4, 10	
40:6–11	
42:1–7	
52:13–53:12	
61:1–2	

4. What peaks and valleys are covered in the book of Isaiah?

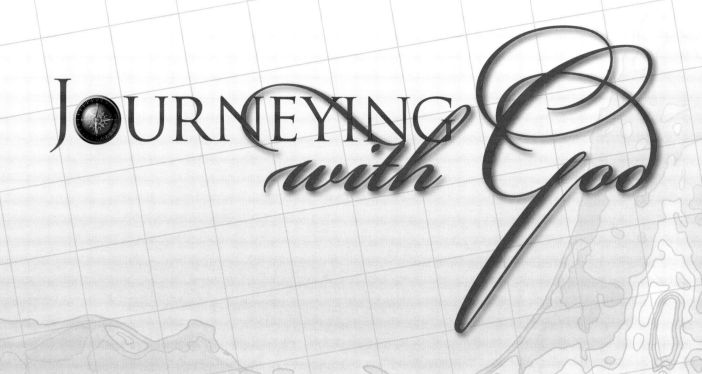

Journeying with God

The Major Prophets—**Jeremiah**

Jeremiah

Key Landmarks

Suggested Reading: 1, 28, 31, 52

Overview

Jeremiah prophesies during the Judah era; his ministry begins during Josiah's reign of spiritual reform. However, the prophet experiences the impenetrable hardness of Judah as the people continue in their sin, even into the Exile era.

Authorship and Date

The author is "Jeremiah son of Hilkiah" (1:1). Internal evidence indicates that the first written material was recorded around 605 BC, the fourth year of Jehoiakim's reign (36:1–2). Evidence throughout the book indicates the recording of prophecies (29:1, 30:2, 36:2, 51:60). Jeremiah apparently compiled these prophecies and edited his work following the 586 BC fall of Jerusalem.

Jeremiah was born in the small town of Anathoth around 646 BC. He probably died in Egypt not long after writing the book. Growing up in a priestly family, he was called into prophetic ministry around 626 BC, the thirteenth year of Josiah's reign (1:2). He seems to have come from relative obscurity, since he was not well known as a prophet during Josiah's reign (2 Kings 22:14).

Message: *Repent in light of Jerusalem's fall.* Jeremiah calls on Judah to repent of its many grievous sins in light of certain judgment coming from Babylon in the north. Though judgment is pervasive in his messages, he still brings promise of a future hope and a new covenant. When the Babylonian captivity becomes certain, Jeremiah calls on Judah to submit to the Babylonians. He makes this plea despite harsh opposition from the lying prophets and the unyielding Judean kings. The book closes with a record of prophecies against the enemies of Judah, climaxing with the destruction of powerful Babylon.

Taking the Journey

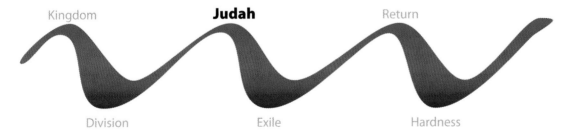

Kingdom   **Judah**   Return

Division   Exile   Hardness

 **Finding Our Way**

1. Read Jeremiah 1:4–10. Summarize what happened when the Lord called Jeremiah.

2. Read and summarize Jeremiah's personal revelations in 10:23–24, 11:18–12:6, 15:10–18, 17:9–18, 18:18–23, and 20:7–18.

3. Study the following passages; record the symbols and describe the lessons those symbols teach: 13:1–11, 16:1–9, 18:1–8, 19:1–13, and 32:6–44.

4. Read Jeremiah 31:31–37 and Hebrews 8:8–12. List some of the benefits of the new covenant that Christians enjoy today.

5. What peaks and valleys are covered in the book of Jeremiah?

Journeying with God

The Major Prophets—
Lamentations

Lamentations

Key Landmarks

Suggested Reading: Lamentations 1–5

Overview
The book of Lamentations is made up of five mournful songs that poetically describe the aftermath of Jerusalem's destruction by Babylon.

Authorship and Date
Though the book itself does not specify an author, several internal clues point to Jeremiah as the author. Themes and phrases in Lamentations match those found in Jeremiah (Jeremiah 9:1, 18 and Lamentations 1:16; Jeremiah 30:14 and Lamentations 1:2; Jeremiah 49:12 and Lamentations 4:21), and Jeremiah was known as a composer of lamentations (2 Chronicles 35:25). If Jeremiah is designated as the author, the final composition and compilation date must then fall between the Babylonian siege of Jerusalem (586 BC) and Jeremiah's flight to Egypt after Gedaliah's assassination (583–582 BC).

Message: *Mourning for Jerusalem and its people.* The book of Lamentations mourns the devastating judgment upon Jerusalem for its sins. The judgment came as the fulfillment of curses in Deuteronomy 28. The city inhabitants finally recognized the total devastation their sins had brought them, but they knew that at that point there was no hope of mercy from the Lord.

Taking the Journey

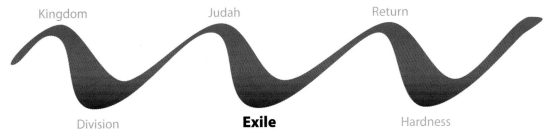

Kingdom   Judah   Return

Division   **Exile**   Hardness

Finding Our Way

1. Compare the five songs of Lamentations with Deuteronomy 28. Look for similar phrases and concepts, and make a chart showing the parallel elements. Then summarize your observations and thoughts in a final paragraph.

2. What do you think is the significance of the third song (chapter 3) in this book?

3. What peaks and valleys are covered in the book of Lamentations?

JOURNEYING with God

The Major Prophets—**Ezekiel**

Ezekiel

Key Landmarks

Suggested Reading: Ezekiel 1–3, 4–5, 37

Overview
The prophet Ezekiel was carried to Babylon eleven years before the destruction of Jerusalem. From his exiled position, he saw in a vision the spiritual contamination of the temple and its coming destruction. God also allowed him to prophesy about the future restoration of the temple.

Authorship and Date
The authorship of Ezekiel is confirmed by two specific references to him in the book: 1:3 and 24:24. Ezekiel began his prophetic ministry in the fifth year (593 BC) of Jehoiachin's exile (1:2). His last dated prophecy came in 571 BC (29:17). He began his ministry at age thirty (1:1), ministering at the same time Jeremiah was prophesying in Jerusalem. Ezekiel prophesied to the Jewish exiles in captivity when Jeremiah was prophesying in Jerusalem and when Daniel was serving in the royal Babylonian courts.

Message: *Priestly warning of judgment and promise of future restoration.*
Ezekiel reminds the exiles that their sins had produced the devastating judgment they are experiencing. Yet within that judgment message is a ray of hope: the promised vengeance on enemies, the restoration of the nation in the land, and the revival of righteous sacrificial worship in a new temple.

Taking the Journey

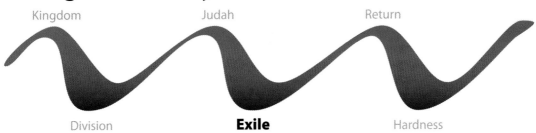

Kingdom   Judah   Return

Division   **Exile**   Hardness

Finding Our Way

1. In your own words, describe Ezekiel's vision (1:4–28). What does this vision reveal about God?

2. Describe the symbolic acts Ezekiel used in chapters 4–5. What does each symbolize?

3. Trace the movement of the glory of God in the following key passages: Ezekiel 9:3–4, 10:18–19, 11:22–23, 43:1–5, and 44:4. What do these passages teach about judgment and restoration? How do these visions fit the message of the book?

4. Summarize the judgments against the nations addressed in Ezekiel 25–32.

5. What are the two visions in chapter 37? What do they teach about Judah's future?

6. What peaks and valleys are covered in the book of Ezekiel?

JOURNEYING *with* God

The Major Prophets—**Daniel**

Daniel

Key Landmarks

Suggested Reading: Daniel 1–7, 9, 12

Overview
Like Lamentations and Ezekiel, the book of Daniel records prophecies delivered during the Exile era. Daniel was taken captive to Babylon as a young man and ministered through the entire Exile period.

Authorship and Date
The book claims that Daniel is its author (8:1, 9:2, 22, 10:2). Daniel was a contemporary of Ezekiel (Ezekiel 14:14, 20, 28:3). His reference to the reign of Cyrus (Daniel 6:28) could place the composition of the book around 530 BC, a few years after Cyrus' conquest of Babylon (539 BC). Daniel was likely a young man when he came to Babylon in 605 BC. Therefore, his prophetic ministry spanned more than seventy years, the entire length of the Babylonian captivity.

Message: *God's sovereign plan and rule for His people and the world.*
The book of Daniel carries the overriding theme of God's sovereign rule. God protected faithful Daniel and the three loyal Hebrews. God governs the reigns of Gentile powers, and God will bring the history of Israel to its fulfillment. God will abolish all earthly powers and establish the Messiah as the supreme ruler of the world.

Taking the Journey

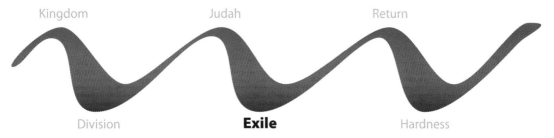

Kingdom   Judah   Return

Division   **Exile**   Hardness

Finding Our Way

1. Describe two of the ways Daniel and his friends demonstrated their trust in God.

2. Compare the vision of the image (2) with the vision of the beasts (7). Both describe the Gentile nations that dominated Israel. Describe each element of the image, each beast, and each corresponding kingdom, and then tell what these symbols say about each of the kingdoms.

Vision and symbols	Description of symbols	Kingdoms	Meaning
Statue			
Head			
Chest and arms			
Belly and thighs			
Legs			
Feet			
Beasts			
Lion			
Bear			
Leopard			
Ten-horned monster			

3. What peaks and valleys are covered in the book of Daniel?

Journeying with God

The Minor Prophets

133

Introduction to the Minor Prophets

The Minor Prophets are the twelve shorter prophetic books that end the Old Testament. They are not minor in importance; they are simply shorter in length than the Major Prophets.

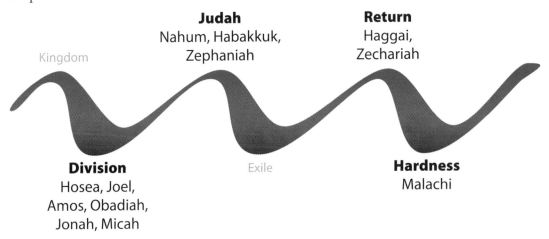

Judah
Nahum, Habakkuk, Zephaniah

Return
Haggai, Zechariah

Kingdom

Division
Hosea, Joel, Amos, Obadiah, Jonah, Micah

Exile

Hardness
Malachi

The chart below shows how the Minor Prophets relate to the history of Israel and Judah and to the historical books of the Old Testament.

Historical Era	Historical Books	Prophetic Books
Division	1 Kings 12–2 Kings 17 2 Chronicles 10–28	Hosea, Amos Joel, Micah Obadiah, Jonah
Judah	2 Kings 18–24 2 Chronicles 29–35	Nahum, Habakkuk, Zephaniah
Exile	2 Kings 25, Chronicles 36 Esther	
Return	Ezra, Nehemiah	Haggai, Zechariah
Hardness		Malachi

The messages of the Minor Prophets share many elements. Though the prophets spoke at different times, in different settings, and with different images, their voices together created a chorus for Israel and Judah to hear and obey. The foundation of the prophets' messages is found in the covenants between God and Israel.

The chart on the following page demonstrates how the basic outline of each book flows from the key elements of the promises and conditions of the covenants.

The Covenant Basis of Messages in the Minor Prophets

Message	Land blessing	Justice promise	Judgment for sin	Hope for restoration	Promise of Messiah
Covenant basis	Abrahamic promise Genesis 12:7: "To your offspring I will give this land."	Abrahamic promise Genesis 12:3: "I will bless those who bless you, and whoever curses you I will curse."	Mosaic covenant Deuteronomy 28:15, 49: "If you do not obey the Lord your God ... these curses will come upon you.... The Lord will bring a nation against you from far away."	Mosaic promise Deuteronomy 30:2-3: "When you ... return to the Lord ... then the Lord your God will restore your fortunes and have compassion on you."	Davidic promise 2 Samuel 7:16: "Your throne will be established forever."
Hosea			1:1-2:13, 4:1-10:15, 11:12-13:16	2:14-3:5, 11:1-11, 14:1-9	
Joel	2:18-27	3:1-16	1:1-2:17	2:28-32, 3:17-21	
Amos		1:1-2:16	3:1-9:10	9:11-15	
Obadiah	1:17-21	1:1-16			
Jonah			1:1-4:11*		
Micah			1:1-2:11 3:1-12 6:1-7:7	2:12-13 4:1-5:15 7:8-20	4:8, 5:2-5
Nahum		1:1-3:19			
Habakkuk		2:2-3:19	1:1-2:1		
Zephaniah		1:1-3, 1:14-18, 2:1-15	1:4-13, 3:1-9	3:10-20	
Haggai		2:20-22	1:1-15	2:1-19	2:7
Zechariah		2:1-13, 6:1-8	5:1-11, 7:1-14	1:1-17, 8:1-23	3:1-4:14, 6:9-15, 9:9-14:21
Malachi			1:1-4:6		

* Jonah is unique in its message, but God's response to Jonah's hatred of Nineveh contains an implied judgment for Israel's contempt for God's sovereign compassion.

Journeying with God

The Minor Prophets
Division-Era Prophets to Israel—
Hosea and Amos

Taking the Journey

Kingdom   Judah   Return

Division   Exile   Hardness

Hosea

 ## Key Landmarks

Suggested Reading: Hosea 1–3, 11–14

Overview
Hosea and Amos prophesied to the northern kingdom of Israel before the fall of its capital, Samaria, in 722 BC. Hosea's ministry continued after that date.

Authorship and Date
Hosea 1:1 identifies the author as "Hosea son of Beeri." According to notes within the book, Hosea began prophesying around the end of Uzziah's reign in Judah (740 BC) and continued until the early years of Hezekiah's reign (715 BC).

Message: *Call of the spurned husband, Yahweh, to His unfaithful bride, Israel.*
Israel has rejected the Lord's love and has committed adultery with idols and foreign nations. For that infidelity, Israel will suffer judgment. Despite Israel's adultery, the Lord in love will restore the nation, and it will be reconciled to Him. This message is communicated both through prophetic messages and through symbolism attached to Hosea's family relationships.

Amos

 ## Key Landmarks

Suggested Reading: Amos 1–2, 7–9

Overview
Amos prophesied to the northern kingdom of Israel before the fall of its capital, Samaria, in 722 BC.

Authorship and Date
The book identifies its author as Amos, a sheepherder from Tekoa, a town located approximately five miles from Bethlehem (1:1, 7:14–15). Amos ministered during the reigns of Uzziah of Judah (792–740 BC) and Jeroboam II of Israel (792–753 BC). The earthquake mentioned in 1:1 may have occurred around 760 BC according to archaeological discoveries at Hazor, placing Amos' oracles around 762 BC.

Message: *Simple shepherd pronounces judgment on Israel's social sins.*
The Lord stirs Amos, a simple shepherd, to proclaim judgment against wealthy Israel for its social sins. Israel's greed, complacency, hypocrisy, and pride will lead to the nation's devastating downfall. But after judgment has purified the people, Israel will be graciously restored to the land.

Finding Our Way

1. Explain the significance of the names of Hosea's children.

2. How does Hosea's relationship with Gomer represent God's relationship with Israel?

3. What emotions does God reveal through Hosea's words? Why do you think God wanted to show those feelings to His people?

4. In chapters 1–2 of Amos, God pronounces judgment on many nations. Pick three of those nations, describe the reasons for God's judgment, and identify the consequences of their wrongdoing.

5. What word pictures does Amos use in chapters 7 and 8? What messages did these word pictures send to the people of Israel?

6. The books of Hosea and Amos both end with a promise of restoration and reconciliation. How does this promise influence your feelings about the promised judgments on Israel?

7. What peaks and valleys are covered in the books of Hosea and Amos?

Journeying with God

The Minor Prophets
Division-Era Prophets to Judah—
Joel and Micah

Taking the Journey

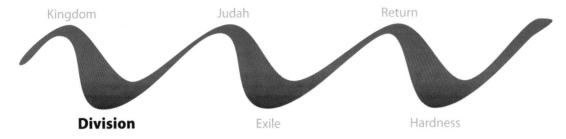

Kingdom   Judah   Return

Division   Exile   Hardness

Joel

Key Landmarks

Suggested Reading: Joel 1–3

Overview
Joel ministered to Judah before the fall of the northern kingdom, Israel.

Authorship and Date
The book is attributed to "Joel son of Pethuel" (1:1). Neither he nor his father is mentioned anywhere else in the Old Testament. The book of Joel is quoted in Acts 2:16–21, and Joel is identified as the author of the quotation. Historical clues lead scholars to tentatively place Joel's prophecies around 830 BC, in the early years of Joash's reign.

Message: *Recent locust plague foreshadows coming judgment.*
Joel employs a recent destructive locust plague as an example to warn of a coming devastating judgment upon Judah. Joel calls on the people to return to the Lord with prayer and fasting in light of this impending judgment. Joel also issues the hope of future salvation and restoration to Judah.

Micah

Key Landmarks

Suggested Reading: Micah 1, 5–7

Overview
Micah ministered to Judah and Israel before the fall of the northern kingdom, Israel.

Authorship and Date
Very little is known about Micah, the book's author. He is from Moresheth (1:1), a Judean village twenty-five miles southwest of Jerusalem, near the Philistine city of Gath. Micah prophesied at the end of the eighth century BC during the reigns of Jotham (750–732 BC), Ahaz (735–716 BC) and Hezekiah (716–687 BC).

Message: *Justice and pardon for God's people Judah.*
Judah stands in God's courtroom accused of breaking the covenant and perverting justice. The people will face a humiliating judgment for their guilt, but in the end they will experience the forgiveness and restoration of the Lord.

Finding Our Way

1. In the first chapter of Joel, how was the invading army (1:6) like a plague of locusts?

2. According to Joel, how can the nation of Judah be saved?

3. Summarize the events associated with the day of the Lord (Joel 2).

4. What references to Jesus can you find in the first few verses of Micah 5?

5. Why was God judging Judah (Micah 6)?

6. Why do you think both Joel and Micah end with promises of restoration and reconciliation? What does this fact tell us about God?

7. What peaks and valleys are covered in the books of Joel and Micah?

JOURNEYING with God

The Minor Prophets
Division-Era Prophets to Foreign Nations—
Obadiah and Jonah

Taking the Journey

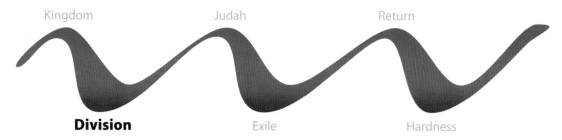

Kingdom   Judah   Return

Division   Exile   Hardness

Obadiah

Key Landmarks

Suggested Reading: Obadiah 1

Overview
Obadiah condemned neighboring Edom for its hostile treatment of Judah.

Authorship and Date
The book names its author as Obadiah (1:1). The book contains few clues to its specific date. The two most likely circumstances that would help date the book are the rebellion of Edom against Judah during Jehoram's reign (2 Kings 8:20–22) and Edom's support for the Babylonian attacks on Judah just before the exile (Psalm 137:7).

Message: *Judgment on Israel's enemy brother.* Obadiah delivers the judgment pronouncement against Edom for its treatment of Israel. In a day of trouble for Judah, Edom had rejoiced in Jerusalem's fall and had even attacked those who were fleeing. In the day of judgment, God will destroy Edom, but Judah will be restored to its land.

Jonah

Key Landmarks

Suggested Reading: Jonah 1–4

Overview
Jonah brought a message of warning to Nineveh, the capital of Assyria. Jonah's message brought a temporary repentance and a stay of God's judgment.

Authorship and Date
The author, Jonah (meaning "dove"), lived in Gath Hepher (2 Kings 14:25). Gath Hepher was in Zebulun, a few miles from Nazareth. He prophesied in the courts of Jeroboam II of Israel. Jonah's prophesied expansion of Jeroboam's territory came to fulfillment.

Message: *Disobedient prophet and distant nation find God's sovereign compassion.* Though focusing on a message of warning to Assyria, Jonah carries a significant message to Israel. First, the book reminds them of the sovereignty of the Lord in accomplishing His purposes. He controls nature and nations. Second, the book highlights the Lord's concern even for the Gentile nations. God shows mercy to all who turn to Him. Third, the book is a subtle indictment of Israel for its disobedience to the Lord and its contempt for His work in the world.

 **Finding Our Way**

1. Against which nation did Obadiah prophesy?

2. Why did Jonah refuse God's command to preach to Nineveh?

3. What do you think the book of Jonah reveals about God?

4. What message does the book of Jonah have for people today?

5. What peaks and valleys are covered in the books of Obadiah and Jonah?

Journeying with God

The Minor Prophets
Judah-Era Prophets—
Habakkuk, Zephaniah, and Nahum

Taking the Journey

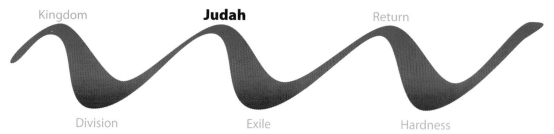

Kingdom   **Judah**   Return

Division   Exile   Hardness

Habakkuk

 ## Key Landmarks

Suggested Reading: Habakkuk 1–3

Overview

Along with Jeremiah, Habakkuk prophesied to Judah after the fall of Israel and before the fall of Judah.

Authorship and Date

The book mentions its author, Habakkuk, twice (1:1, 3:1). It describes him only as "the prophet," perhaps implying that he held the office of prophet (like Amos, who prophesied but who was a shepherd). The superscript (3:1) and subscript (3:19) may also imply that Habakkuk was connected to the temple musicians (1 Chronicles 25:1–8).

The book of Habakkuk gives few clues about its composition date. The Lord was raising up Babylon to punish Judah (1:6), so the book was probably written close to Babylon's 605 BC invasion of Judah. The book also portrays Babylon as a military power (1:6–11, 15–17, 2:5–17). This portrayal probably indicates a date after Babylon had established itself as a world power through its defeat of Egypt at Carchemish (605 BC). Therefore, Habakkuk perhaps prophesied in the span between the historic victory of Babylon at Carchemish and its subsequent invasion of Judah. This possible time span places Habakkuk in the reign of Jehoiakim and makes him a contemporary of Jeremiah.

Message: *A prophet questions—then trusts— the Lord's judgment of Judah through Babylon.* Habakkuk wrestles with the justice of God in using wicked Babylon to judge less-wicked Judah. Habakkuk's tension is resolved by the revelation from the Lord that He judges wicked nations as well and by the commitment of Habakkuk to trust his sovereign God in any circumstance.

Zephaniah

Key Landmarks

Suggested Reading: Zephaniah 1–3

Overview
Along with Jeremiah, Zephaniah ministered to Judah after Israel's fall and before the exile of Judah.

Authorship and Date
Zephaniah opens the book by tracing his own genealogy four generations back to Hezekiah, a well-known reforming king of Judah. Zephaniah most likely prophesied during the early years of Josiah's reign, beginning in 640 or 639 BC.

Message: *Judgment and restoration in the day of the Lord.*
Zephaniah proclaims the coming day of the Lord's wrath. God will judge the nations for their wickedness and will purify Judah of its corruption and rejection. The remnant of cleansed people will be redeemed and restored to the land, where they will be exalted among all nations.

Nahum

Key Landmarks

Suggested Reading: Nahum 1–3

Overview
Nahum, like Jonah, brought a message of warning to Nineveh, the capital of Assyria. Nahum's later message announced the final destruction of that nation.

Authorship and Date
The author, Nahum (1:1), is unknown outside his book. Nahum refers to the fall of Thebes (663 BC) as already having occurred (3:8) and implies that the fall of Nineveh (612 BC) is imminent.

Message: *Promised flood of judgment upon Assyria.*

The revival that came to Nineveh through Jonah's preaching was short-lived. Because Assyria had ravaged many nations—especially Israel—and then had threatened Judah, the Lord will bring final judgment upon Assyria. Nahum foretells the overwhelming flood of judgment that the Lord will bring upon that nation in punishment for its treatment of His chosen people.

 **Finding Our Way**

1. What did Habakkuk want God to do with Judah?

2. What answer did God give Habakkuk?

3. How did Habakkuk respond to God's answer?

4. How had Habakkuk's attitude changed by the end of the book?

5. Name some of the things that will happen on the day of the Lord according to Zephaniah.

6. According to Zephaniah, what will happen to Judah after the day of the Lord?

7. How are Jonah and Nahum linked?

8. What peaks and valleys are covered in the books of Habakkuk, Zephaniah, and Nahum?

Journeying with God

The Minor Prophets
Return-Era and Hardness-Era Prophets—
Haggai, Zechariah, and Malachi

Taking the Journey

Kingdom   Judah   **Return**

Division   Exile   **Hardness**

Haggai

Key Landmarks

Suggested Reading: Haggai 1–2

Overview
Haggai and Zechariah prophesied during the temple rebuilding recorded in the book of Ezra.

Authorship and Date
The book names its author as Haggai. Haggai is said to have encouraged the Jews to rebuild the temple after their captivity (Ezra 5:1, 6:14). Haggai was the first to prophesy to the postexilic community. His specifically dated prophecies were delivered between August and December of 520 BC. They came at a time when the Jews had returned from exile and were struggling to complete the temple. After beginning to work on the temple (Ezra 3:8–13), the Jews halted the work because of outside opposition. Then they began to pursue their own interests instead of completing God's house. Haggai and Zechariah then exhorted the people to return to the work and finish the temple. The temple was completed in 516 BC, 70 years after its 586 BC destruction.

Message: *Admonishment and encouragement to complete the temple.*
The book of Haggai consists of a series of five messages designed to admonish and encourage the remnant of Jews to complete the temple so that they would receive the blessing of the Lord.

Zechariah

Key Landmarks

Suggested Reading: Zechariah 9–14

Overview
Haggai and Zechariah prophesied during the temple rebuilding recorded in the book of Ezra.

Authorship and Date
Zechariah was the son of Berekiah, son of Iddo (1:1). Iddo was among the heads of the tribe of Levi who returned from the captivity (Nehemiah 12:4, 16). Thus Zechariah served not only as a prophet but also as a priest in Israel. Zechariah began his ministry (1:1) in the eighth month of the second year of Darius (November 520 BC). He began his ministry just two or three months after Haggai's first prophecy. The last dated prophecy of Zechariah was in 518 BC (7:1), though he may have prophesied as late as 480 BC in light of the reference to Greece in 9:13.

Message: *Temple-building encouragement and the temple's awesome messianic future.* Along with Haggai, Zechariah encourages the returning remnant in their rebuilding efforts. Zechariah encourages the people by challenging them to repent and to be cleansed and by foretelling the Lord's great future for Israel. This future will climax in the Messiah's universal and holy rule.

Malachi

Key Landmarks

Suggested Reading: Malachi 1–4

Overview
Malachi confronted the hardening hearts faced by both Ezra and Nehemiah.

Authorship and Date
Nothing is known of Malachi, the author, except that he was a contemporary of Nehemiah. His name means "my messenger." He was the last of the Old Testament prophets to minister until John the Baptist, whose coming is prophesied by Malachi (4:5–6). Regarding its date of composition, the book gives several clues. The book presupposes that the temple has been rebuilt and that sacrifices are again being offered. The Persian name for governor (*pechah*, 1:8) places the date within the period of Persian rule over Israel (539–333 BC). The nation had deteriorated into many religious and social sins, perhaps the very ones Nehemiah faced upon his return. For these reasons, many place the date of the book in the Hardness era after the returns led by Ezra (458 BC) and Nehemiah (444 BC).

Message: *Challenge to return to the Lord and receive blessing through the coming Messiah.* Coming on the scene after the revivals of the rebuilt temple had degenerated into spiritual apathy and moral failure, Malachi challenges the lethargic remnant to repent and return to the Lord. His challenges take the form of a series of questions. The Jewish remnant's repentance and obedience will bring blessing rather than judgment from the coming Messiah.

 **Finding Our Way**

1. How were the ministries of Haggai and Zechariah related?

2. Name some of Zechariah's prophecies that are related to Christ's first advent.

3. Why was Christ's second coming important to Haggai and Zechariah?

4. Explain two of the seven key questions found in Malachi.

5. According to Malachi, who will come before the day of the Lord arrives? Which New Testament character fulfilled this prophecy?

6. Which peaks and valleys are covered by the books of Haggai, Zechariah, and Malachi?